CHANGE YOUR WORDS - CHANGE YOUR WORLD

~ PHIL M JONES

DEDICATED TO EVERY PARENT ON THE PLANET THAT IS
BRAVE ENOUGH TO DARE THEIR CHILD DREAM, SUPPORT
THEM ON THE JOURNEY AND CATCH THEM WHEN THEY FALL.

~ PHIL M JONES

THE MAGIC OF WORDS
Published by Box of Tricks 2021

All inquiries should be directed to
www.PhilMJones.com

ISBN-13: 978-0-578-96637-3 Paperback
ISBN-13: 978-0-578-96638-0 Hardcover

THE MAGIC OF WORDS

Phil M Jones
& Eevi Jones

Words paint a thousand pictures,
through stories, tales, and more.
Creating imaginary worlds
to jump into and explore.

Worlds where kings and queens are mighty,
with their castles, crowns, and throne.
Where girls and boys are mighty too,
with magic words all of their own.

Beginnings, middles, endings,
words formed and put together.
Created from the alphabet,
letter after letter.

So tiny, yet such might.
Strong enough to open gates.
For a simple *Please* and *Thank You*
is sometimes all it takes.

Our *Pleases* and our *Thank Yous* –
they're the world's magic words. That's true!
But did you know that other words
have magic powers too?

The words we *choose* to use,
the words we think and say,
these words affect our feelings
in a very special way.

Words can make us feel amazing,
make us feel all proud and strong.
When filled with heart and kindness,
words make us feel like we belong.

Words can make us brave,
turning a *no* into a *yes*.
Where "I can't" becomes "I can."
Where we take action nonetheless.

Changing moods from red to green,
from frowns and tears to smiles.
From giving up to pushing through,
turning small steps into miles.

But words can also make us feel
angry, lonely, mad.
Make us lose our confidence.
Make us feel upset or even sad.

So before words leave our lips
we must make sure that they won't hurt.
For words can't be unspoken.
They cannot be unheard.

Words always find their way
into our heads and our hearts.
They write countless little stories,
with new endings and new starts.

For words are rather sticky.
Once spoken they get stuck.
They stick like sticky lollipops,
like boots get stuck in muck.

You have a word, you speak a word.
You keep it, or you break it.
You fight with words, make up with words.
You live by it, and give it.

And once it has been given,
you must not break your word.
For a promise is a promise,
or it will lose its worth.

Words can build us up and tear us down,
help us connect and share ideas;
make us feel lonely and unheard,
or fill a room with cheers.

Whether spoken, read, or heard
through song or book or lens;
words can be so powerful,
break bonds, or make new friends.

So know the power of your words!
Be careful what you say.
Be careful *how* you say the things
you share and speak each day.

With your daily choice of words
you get to change the world.
And that's the magic power held
by every boy and every girl.

ABOUT THE AUTHORS

Phil M Jones is a Dreamer. Someone who has imagined an alternate reality and then been brave enough to build it. He imagined his beautiful family, having homes in two of the greatest cities in the world and even his made up job of being a professional speaker and author.

Right now, he is making up his next chapter of life fueled by his own over active imagination and relentless optimism.

To learn more about Phil and his mission, visit www.PhilMJones.com.

Eevi Jones is a Vietnamese-American *USA Today* and *Wall Street Journal* bestselling writer and award-winning children's book author.

She lives near D.C. with her husband and their two boys.

Eevi can be found at www.BravingTheWorldBooks.com.

OTHER BOOKS BY PHIL M JONES

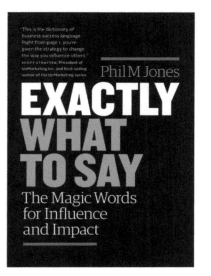

There is a book that helps grown ups learn more about the power of words too.

It has helped a GAZZILLION people, and is concise and to the point so that even the busiest of people can implement its actionable advice right away.

So parents, if you have ever found yourself lost for words or wondered *Exactly What to Say*, then grab yourself a copy of this.

Available wherever books are sold.